Joined at the Funny Bone

Joined at the Funny Bone

A collection of cartoons by Ralph Dunagin and Dana Summers

Foreword by Charley Reese

Sentinel Communications Company
Orlando/1990

Copyright © 1990
Sentinel Communications Company
633 North Orange Avenue
Orlando, Florida 32801

Cover illustration by Ralph Dunagin

ISBN 0-941263-18-5

Printed in the United States by Walsworth Publishing Co.

First edition October 1990

To Mildred and Mary Jane,
who make the deadlines
bearable.

Special thanks to:
Jane Healy, John Haile, Mike Murphy,
George Biggers, Charley Reese,
Eileen Schechner, David Wersinger,
Dick Locher, Doug Marlette,
Washington Post Writers Group
and North America Syndicate.

After you've finished reading this, you can enjoy the work of two of the most talented cartoonists in America. You'll get what only great cartoonists can give you — laughs and insight.

Some people think cartooning is all about drawing, but it is really all about seeing and understanding. That's why writers are jealous. Ralph Dunagin and Dana Summers can take a situation, size it up, and render a combination of perfect summation and commentary with a few strokes of the pen and eight or 10 words. A writer would take thousands of words and still not do it so well.

What it takes to be a great cartoonist is not just drawing skill but keen observation, wisdom and intelligence. Nothing can be boiled down or reduced to its essence unless it is first understood.

And that's enough of the serious stuff. These two guys somewhat resemble their work. Dana Summers is a brash, urban type who can't walk across a small room without making three wisecracks. Ralph Dunagin looks like a country gentleman, is unfailingly courteous and generally sober in appearance until he laughs. Then he falls apart. After you've been around Ralph awhile, you get the feeling that he puts a lot of effort into keeping a straight face.

Like the odd couple, the Massachusetts-born Summers and the Mississippi-born Dunagin work great together, each striking sparks off the other. It's the wise-acre of the streets in partnership with the country wit. You'll enjoy their work, but I'm luckier than you are. I work next to them. Hearing stories of Ralph's dog, Bumper, and of Dana's battle with a spider (the spider won) and watching these two guys do their magic day after day is a daily dose of fun. And they always have a store of jokes.

So sit back and enjoy. None of us can solve the world's problems. But these two guys sure can make it fun to think about them.

Charley Reese
Orlando Sentinel columnist
Syndicated by King Features

Ollie North testifies.

"AND ON THE BEACH, MORE MEDICAL WASTE...
A BEEPER AND AN OLD SET OF GOLF CLUBS."

"OKAY, SO I OCCASIONALLY CONSULT THE
STARS... BOB HOPE, CHARLTON HESTON,
FRANK SINATRA..."

3

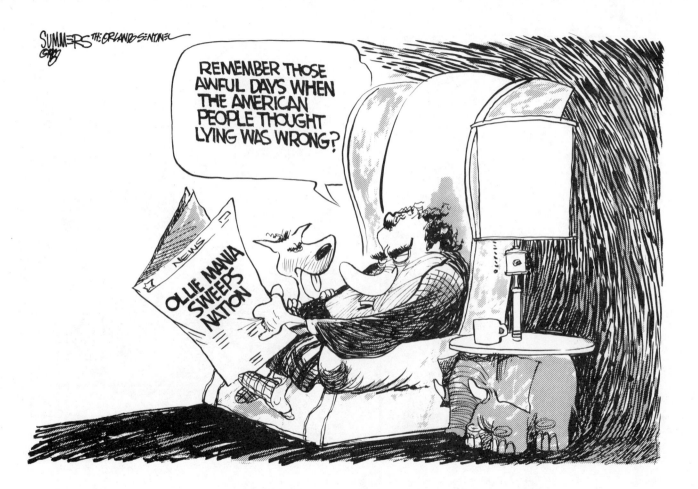

4

"YES, I THINK HE KNEW, BUT I DON'T THINK HE KNOWS THAT HE KNEW."

"I WAS PRESIDENT?"

"THE COMMITTEE CALLS ORAL ROBERTS TO BRING WILLIAM CASEY BACK TO TESTIFY."

"IT TAKES A BIG MAN TO ADMIT HIS ADVISERS WERE WRONG!"

6

7

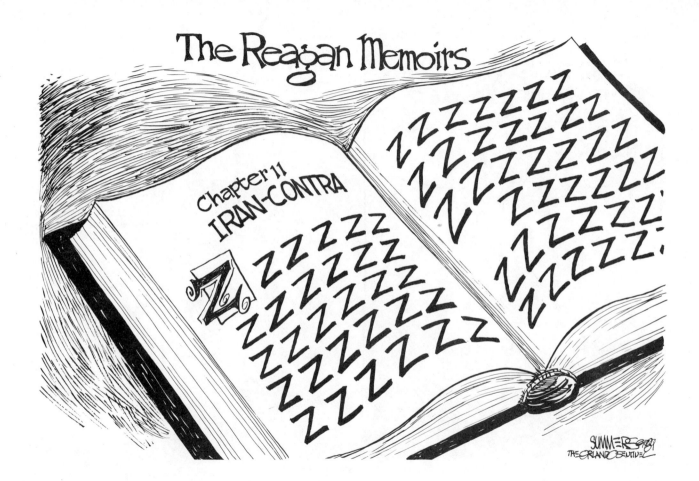

8

9

"MEN, I'M CONCERNED THAT THIS UPROAR OVER HOUSE ETHICS COULD TURN INTO A WITCH HUNT!"

"MY AIDE HAS AN EXCELLENT RECORD ... NO CONVICTIONS!"

11

Senate confirmation hearings give John Tower the breath test.

"THE 1990 CENSUS WILL RESULT IN ADDING A CONGRESSMAN FOR THIS AREA ... ONE OF THE PRICES WE PAY FOR GROWTH."

"DEAR, HOW DO I FEEL ABOUT WOMEN IN COMBAT?"

THE HONORABLE SPEAKER OF THE HOUSE.

Jim Wright's problems escalate.

FIRST SHOT IN THE WAR ON DRUGS

15

"OUR CAR HAS BEEN RECALLED... WE ARE TO VERY, VERY CAREFULLY DRIVE IT BACK TO THE DEALER..."

"WELL, HERE'S YOUR TROUBLE... YOUR WARRANTY HAS RUN OUT."

President Bush displays a bag of crack during a televised speech on drugs.

"WOULD YOU TWO PLEASE TALK A LITTLE LOUDER? THE SOUND FROM THE MOVIE OCCASIONALLY DROWNS YOU OUT."

"WE'RE LOOKING FOR SOMETHING DISGUSTING FOR OUR LIVING ROOM."

DRUG TRAFFICKING ROUTES

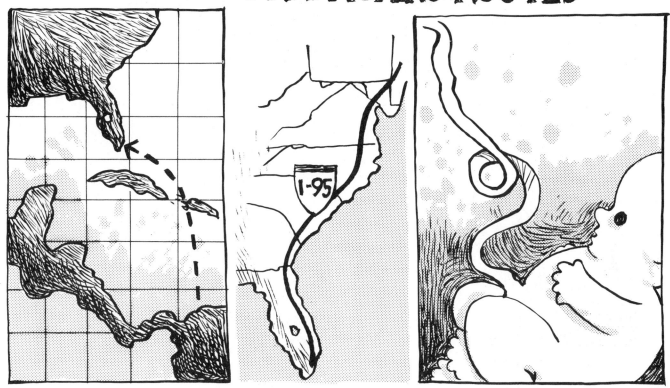

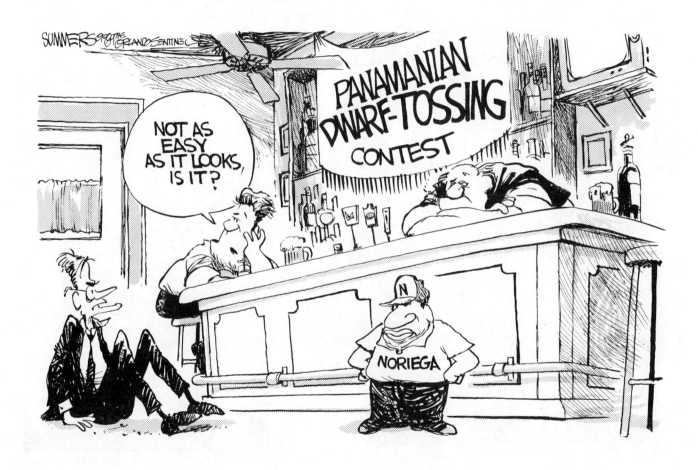

"OKAY, WHO HASN'T HAD HORSESHOE DETAIL?"

22

23

"DID YOU KNOW THAT YOU AND SUPERMAN ARE THE SAME AGE?"

"NO, YOU MAY NOT HAVE CALIFORNIA!"

25

"GREAT! THE BAGGAGE HANDLERS BROKE ALL THE SIGNS!"

"HOW OLD IS THIS PLANE ANYWAY? THEY'RE PUTTING GERITOL IN THE FUEL TANKS!"

Disney signs a deal with Jim Henson.

"GOOD EVENING, SIR. DUE TO SOME MINOR CROSS-WIRING IN THE AIRCRAFT, YOU ARE THE PILOT OF THIS FLIGHT."

"FLIGHT 943 TO NEW YORK IS NOW ARRIVING AT CHAPTER, ER, GATE 11."

31

"MALL! MALL!..."

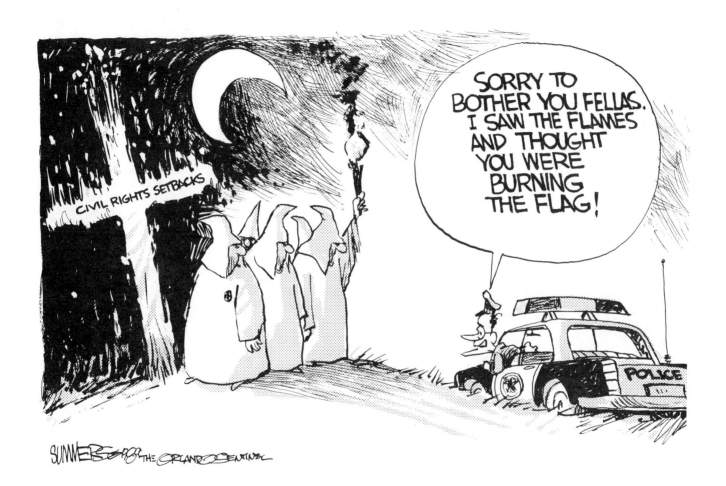

33

34

"A TELEVISION EVANGELIST HAS BEEN SEEN WITH HIS WIFE!"

"KEEP AN EYE ON BAKKER'S VISITOR...THERE COULD BE A FILE UNDER THAT MAKEUP."

35

HERITAGE U.S.A. TIME SHARE

JIM BAKKER WATER SLIDE

"AMALGAMATED'S BID CAN NO LONGER BE CONSIDERED A FRIENDLY TAKEOVER ATTEMPT...THEY'VE TAKEN HOSTAGES."

39

"DEAR, DON'T YOU THINK IT'S TIME JUNIOR SUED SOMEONE?"

41

WHY JOHNNY CAN'T READ AND WRITE

"EVERYTHING WE USED TO DO KILLS PEOPLE TODAY."

"IT'S A MEDICAL EMERGENCY... I'M TRYING TO GET THROUGH A MID-LIFE CRISIS!"

44

"WE'D LIKE TO BORROW ENOUGH TO OPEN A SAVINGS ACCOUNT."

"I DON'T GET IT. WE'VE TESTED EVERY DISEASE KNOWN TO MANKIND ON RATS, AND WE STILL HAVE A RAT PROBLEM."

45

46

"IF EVEN HALF OF THE CHARGES BY THE NCAA ARE TRUE, COACH, WHY HAVEN'T WE BEEN WINNING?"

"MANY OF THE PLAYERS WITHDREW OBJECTIONS TO DRUG TESTS WHEN WE ASSURED THEM THAT THEY DIDN'T HAVE TO STUDY FOR THEM."

"LOOKS LIKE THE STATUE OF LIBERTY PLAY, MEL
... WHERE THE EUROPEAN IMMIGRANT COMES
IN AND KICKS A FIELD GOAL."

"YOU CAN'T TELL ME THAT SHOT PUTTER
ISN'T ON STEROIDS."

The thrill of victory becomes the agony of the sleaze.

"THE OLYMPICS COMMITTEE ANNOUNCED TODAY THAT SPUDS MACKENZIE HAS TESTED POSITIVE FOR COORS LIGHT."

"BAXTER, WE REALLY HAVEN'T BEEN HAPPY WITH YOUR PERFORMANCE SINCE YOU FOUNDED THIS COMPANY."

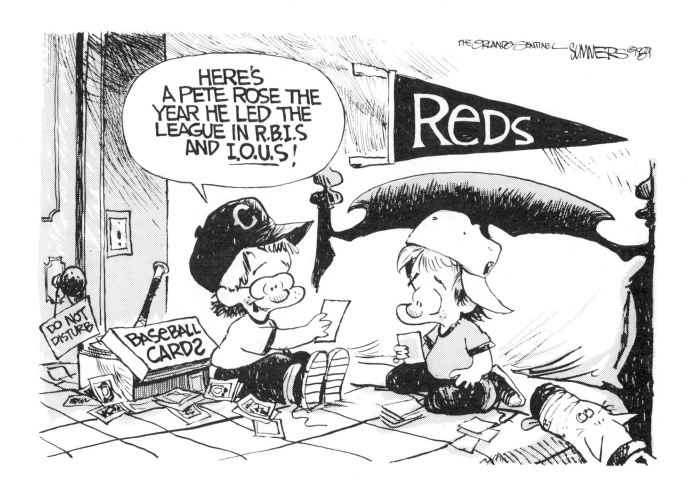

53

"SOMEDAY, MY BOY, THIS WILL ALL BELONG TO YOU ...ASSUMING YOUR HOSTILE TAKEOVER IS SUCCESSFUL."

"WE'RE IN AGREEMENT, THEN, THAT THIS CAN'T BE HAPPENING."

57

FIRSTHRIFT

FOUNDED
1926

BAILED OUT
1989

"I THINK I JUST MERGED FORD WITH GENERAL MOTORS!"

THE ORLANDO SENTINEL

"AND THE NOMINEES ARE: JIMMY SWAGGERT FOR HIS CRYING SCENE,..."

"IF MRS. HELMSLEY IS SENT HERE, I THINK A MINT ON HER PILLOW WOULD BE A NICE TOUCH."

64

"LET ME GET THIS STRAIGHT... THE SOVIETS ARE FINALLY HAVING ELECTIONS, AND THE U.S. GETS ITS FIRST CZAR?"

"ONE OF OUR COMMUNICATIONS SATELLITES JUST DECLARED ITS INDEPENDENCE."

66

The Berlin Wall comes tumbling down and the days of communism seem to be numbered.

"I FELT GUILTY ABOUT FIRING ON THOSE STUDENTS UNTIL I FOUND OUT WE DIDN'T DO IT."

"AT LEAST WE STILL HAVE EACH OTHER, RIGHT, COMRADES? COMRADES?"

East German Shopping Spree

"IS FIRST CHALLENGE TO NEW IMPROVED SOVIET UNION... TO BUILD AN AUTOMOBILE THAT CAN MAKE IT THROUGH THE McDONALD'S DRIVE-THRU."

73

"YES, WE KNOW THE GENERAL SECRETARY VISITED NEW YORK, BUT I REPEAT, TAXI CABS ARE <u>NOT</u> OFFENSIVE WEAPONS!"

"ANYONE WHO HAS EVER PLOWED WOULDN'T BE SO QUICK TO BEAT ALL THE SWORDS INTO PLOWSHARES."

"AND NOW GRANDPA WILL GIVE THANKS FOR OUR GOOD FORTUNES, AND GRANDMA WILL GIVE THE DEMOCRAT RESPONSE."

"WE PREFER THAT YOU STICK TO THE FACTORY-RECOMMENDED DEALER INCENTIVES, WIMBLETON."

"A SURROGATE STORK BROUGHT YOU."

"I'M AFRAID WE'VE MADE A RATHER STARTLING DISCOVERY, MR. FENTON ... YOU'RE A LAWYER."

'VIRTUE IS NOT LEFT TO STAND ALONE. HE WHO PRACTICES IT WILL HAVE NEIGHBORS.' — CONFUCIUS

"I MAY BE A LITTLE LATE, DEAR... NO ONE HAS NOTICED ME ON MY CAR PHONE YET."

"SHE WAS LAST SEEN WEARING IVORY EARRINGS, ALLIGATOR SHOES AND A SEALSKIN JACKET. OUR GUESS IS SHE WAS TAKEN BY POACHERS."

CHINESE STUDENTS

U.S. STUDENTS

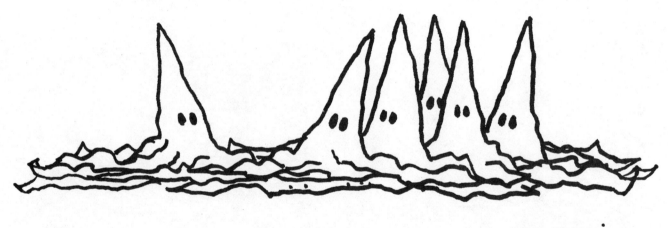

"THAT'S IT, MEN... STAND TALL FOR AMERICA!"

"THESE OLD CARS JUST CAN'T TAKE THE POUNDING OF THE NEW STEREO SYSTEMS."

Salman Rushdie hides out.

89

90

"IT SEEMS THAT THE ONLY THING KEEPING US TOGETHER IS NEITHER ONE OF US HAS AIDS."

"WE'VE ALREADY HELD HANDS FOR THE HOMELESS."

East Germans convert their currency.

"ACCORDING TO THIS REPORT, ONLY 3.6% OF ALL DOGGY BAGS ACTUALLY GET TO THE DOGS!"

"WE'VE BEEN UNABLE TO CONFIRM REPORTS THAT THREE OBESE PEOPLE TRIED TO EAT DICK GREGORY."

Gorby begins his new American-style presidency.

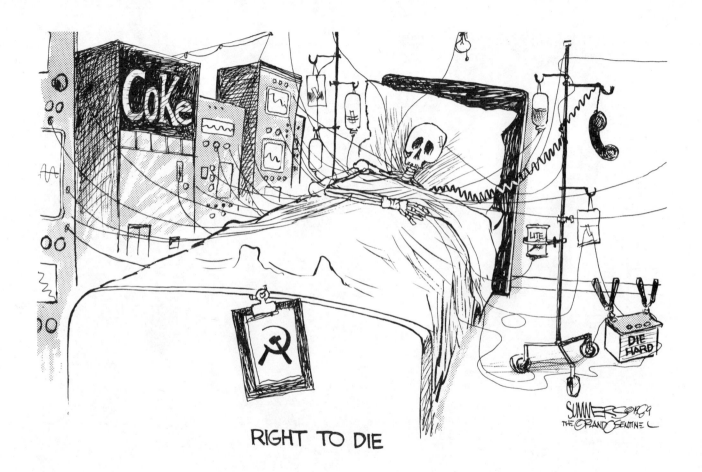

RIGHT TO DIE

"I TELL YOU, HARVE, THE AWESOME POWER OF TELEVISION IS FRIGHTENING!"

CRIME IN AMERICA

"AMERICANS WILL SPEND $3 MILLION ON MACE THIS YEAR... THE BAD NEWS IS THEY WILL NEED MORE."

"IT'S TIME FOR US TO STAND UP AND DEMAND THAT THE JAPANESE TAKE LESS PRIDE IN THEIR WORK!"

"GUESS WHAT."

Gorbachev cuts off supplies to Lithuania.

"WOULD YOU HOLD FOR THE GREAT COMMUNICATOR, PLEASE?"

"IT'S THE EPA'S ANSWER TO ACID RAIN...TUMS."

INFIDEL

Cuba continues to resist change.

"APPARENTLY LYING TO CONGRESS IS MUCH MORE SERIOUS THAN HAVING CONGRESS LIE TO YOU."

"THIS IS THE DAY I MARCH RIGHT IN THERE AND ASK MYSELF FOR A RAISE!"

"OUR JOB IS TO PUT A STOP TO VOODOO ECONOMICS... WE'RE GOING TO NEED A LOT OF CHICKEN BLOOD."

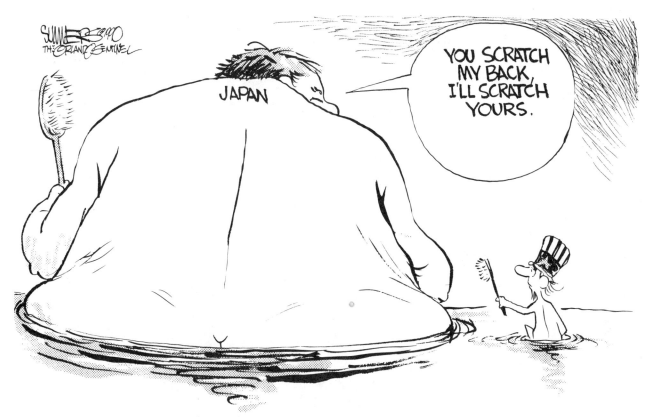

TRADE AGREEMENT

"GO EASY WITH THE BOILING OIL... IT COULD BE HARMFUL TO THE FISH IN THE MOAT."

"DARN IT, FORNSBY, I WON'T HAVE A SPEECH WRITER OF MINE RIPPING OFF SOMEONE ELSE'S SPEECH WRITER'S SPEECHES!"

Poor management forces the great New York City department store into financial trouble.

113

Imelda Marcos on trial

"WELL, THAT SHOULD TAKE EVERYONE'S MIND OFF AIR POLLUTION FOR A WHILE."

"THERE I WAS, ROUGHING IT IN ALASKA, SURVIVING IN THE WILDERNESS, WHEN —WHAM— OUT OF THE BLUE, I WAS CLEANED BY A GANG OF ENVIRONMENTALISTS!"

117

"WE'RE GETTING A BETTER CLASS OF LITTER
... THIS IS AN IMPORTED BEER."

"WHAT HAPPENED? EXXON PULL OUT ALREADY?"

119

"THE GOOD NEWS IS THE FLOOD MAY PUT OUT SOME OF THE FOREST FIRES."

"OH NO! NOT ON THE WEEKEND!"

121

ALASKA

123

"OH, YEAH? WELL, MY FATHER COULD TAKE OVER YOUR FATHER'S COMPANY BEFORE YOUR FATHER COULD GO INTO CHAPTER ELEVEN!"

"YOUR HONOR, MAY I REMIND THE COURT THAT MY CLIENTS OWN THIS BUILDING?"

"STAY AWAY FROM STRESS TESTS."

127

"HMM... I WONDER WHAT WE MEANT BY THIS."

"GOOD NEWS FOR THE CREW OF LAST MONTH'S DISCOVERY FLIGHT... THEIR LUGGAGE HAS BEEN FOUND!"

129

130

"IN DEFENSE OF HUD, IT SURE MADE A DIFFERENCE IN <u>OUR</u> HOUSING SITUATION."

"LET'S NOT WORK SO HARD GROWING OUR OWN SAFE-TO-EAT VEGETABLES THAT WE BREATHE TOO MUCH OF THIS AIR."

A freed Mandela struggles to unite South Africa.

133

134

"WHAT IF, WHEN THEY CLEAN UP THE SMOG, WE DON'T LIKE WHAT WE SEE?"

President Bush abandons his 'no new taxes' promise.

137

"THINK OF THIS COMPANY AS AIR FORCE ONE, WIMBLY, AND YOU ARE BROCCOLI."

"AND AFTER OUR ENTHUSIASTIC SUPPORT OF EARTH DAY!"

Iran receives unlikely earthquake aid.

NASA's problems continue.

142

"YOU WOULDN'T HAPPEN TO HAVE 32 SETS OF JUMPER CABLES, WOULD YOU?"

"WHAT COULD I HAVE SEEN ON TV THAT WOULD MAKE ME DO SUCH A THING?"

144

"WAIT. NEVER MIND, IT'S JUST THE FLAG."

146

147

"WELL, THAT'S THAT... DO YOU HAVE THE REPLACEMENT READY?"

HABITAT

148

Roseanne Barr's rendition of 'The Star-Spangled Banner' raises eyebrows and tempers.

"IT WOULD BE HARD TO GO BACK TO BEING A MILLIONAIRE AFTER YOU'VE BEEN A BILLIONAIRE."

"NOW WHAT? I WRITE SPY NOVELS, AND THERE AREN'T ANY BAD GUYS LEFT!"